Meet big **B** and little **b**.

Bb

Trace each letter with your finger and say its name.

B is for

bear

B is also for

bike

ball

bird

balloon

Bb Story

This **b**ear can ride a **b**ike.

This **b**ear can **b**ounce a **b**all.

But can this **b**ear fly with the **b**irds in the sky?

He sees a **b**oy and **b**uys
a **b**ig **b**unch of **b**alloons.

Yes, this **b**ear can fly with
the **b**irds in the **b**eautiful sky.
Bye, **b**ye!